Working Papers (Chapters 12-25)

Accounting

TWENTY-FIRST EDITION

CARL S. WARREN

Professor Emeritus of Accounting

University of Georgia, Athens

JAMES M. REEVE

Professor of Accounting

University of Tennessee, Knoxville

PHILIP E. FESS

Professor Emeritus of Accountancy

University of Illinois, Champaign-Urbana

Australia · Canada · Mexico · Singapore · Spain · United Kingdom · United States

Working Papers to accompany Accounting, 21e Chapters 12-25

Carl S. Warren, James M. Reeve, Philip E. Fess

VP/Editorial Director:
Jack W. Calhoun

VP/Editor-in-Chief:
George Werthman

Publisher:
Rob Dewey

Executive Editor:
Sharon Oblinger

Developmental Editor:
Erin Joyner

Marketing Manager:
Keith Chassé

Production Editor:
Heather Mann

Manufacturing Coordinator:
Doug Wilke

Technology Project Editor:
Sally Nieman

Media Editor:
Robin Browning

Design Project Manager:
Michelle Kunkler

Production Services:
Gail Strietmann

Cover Designer:
Michael H. Stratton

Illustrator:
Matsu

Printer:
Thomson West
Eagan, MN

Printed in the United States of America
1 2 3 4 5 07 06 05 04

ISBN: 0-324-20376-4

For more information contact South-Western,
5191 Natorp Boulevard,
Mason, Ohio, 45040.
Or you can visit our Internet site at:
http://www.swlearning.com

Name ____________________

EXERCISE 12-1

Description	1st Year	2nd Year	3rd Year	4th Year	5th Year
Total Preferred Stock					
Total Common Stock					
Dividend Totals	$0	$40,000	$80,000	$120,000	$140,000
Per Share—Preferred					
Per Share—Common					

EXERCISE 12-2

Description	1st Year	2nd Year	3rd Year	4th Year	5th Year
Total Preferred Stock					
Total Common Stock					
Dividend Totals	$0	$45,000	$110,000	$130,000	$180,000
Per Share—Preferred					
Per Share—Common					

EXERCISE 12-3

a.

JOURNAL PAGE

	DATE		DESCRIPTION	POST. REF.	DEBIT	CREDIT	
1							1
2							2
3							3
4							4
5							5
6							6
7							7
8							8
9							9
10							10
11							11

b. ____________________

EXERCISE 12-4

a.

JOURNAL

PAGE

	DATE	DESCRIPTION	POST. REF.	DEBIT	CREDIT	
1						1
2						2
3						3
4						4
5						5
6						6
7						7
8						8
9						9
10						10
11						11
12						12
13						13
14						14
15						15
16						16
17						17
18						18

b. ______________________________

EXERCISE 12-5

JOURNAL

PAGE

	DATE	DESCRIPTION	POST. REF.	DEBIT	CREDIT	
1						1
2						2
3						3
4						4
5						5
6						6
7						7
8						8
9						9
10						10

Name ______________________________

EXERCISE 12-6

a.–c.

JOURNAL PAGE

DATE		DESCRIPTION	POST. REF.	DEBIT	CREDIT

EXERCISE 12-7

JOURNAL PAGE

DATE		DESCRIPTION	POST. REF.	DEBIT	CREDIT

EXERCISE 12-8

JOURNAL

PAGE

DATE		DESCRIPTION	POST. REF.	DEBIT	CREDIT

EXERCISE 12-9

a.

JOURNAL

PAGE

DATE		DESCRIPTION	POST. REF.	DEBIT	CREDIT

EXERCISE 12-9, Concluded

b. ______________________

c. ______________________

EXERCISE 12-10

a.

JOURNAL

PAGE

	DATE		DESCRIPTION	POST. REF.	DEBIT	CREDIT	
1							1
2							2
3							3
4							4
5							5
6							6
7							7
8							8
9							9
10							10
11							11
12							12
13							13
14							14
15							15

b. ______________________

c. ______________________

d. ______________________

EXERCISE 12-11

a.

JOURNAL PAGE

DATE		DESCRIPTION	POST. REF.	DEBIT	CREDIT

b.

c.

d.

EXERCISE 12-12

a.

b.

Name ______________________________

EXERCISE 12-13

	Assets	Liabilities	Stockholders' Equity
(1) Declaring a cash dividend	________	________	________
(2) Paying the cash dividend declared in (1)	________	________	________
(3) Authorizing and issuing stock certificates in a stock split..	________	________	________
(4) Declaring a stock dividend	________	________	________
(5) Issuing stock certificates for the stock dividend declared in (4).......................................	________	________	________

EXERCISE 12-14

JOURNAL PAGE

	DATE		DESCRIPTION	POST. REF.	DEBIT	CREDIT	
1							1
2							2
3							3
4							4
5							5
6							6
7							7
8							8
9							9

EXERCISE 12-15

a. (1) and (2)

JOURNAL PAGE

	DATE		DESCRIPTION	POST. REF.	DEBIT	CREDIT	
1							1
2							2
3							3
4							4
5							5
6							6
7							7
8							8
9							9

EXERCISE 12-15, Concluded

b. (1) Total paid-in capital: ____________________

(2) Total retained earnings: ____________________

(3) Total stockholders' equity: ____________________

c. (1) Total paid-in capital: ____________________

(2) Total retained earnings: ____________________

(3) Total stockholders' equity: ____________________

EXERCISE 12-16

JOURNAL PAGE

DATE		DESCRIPTION	POST. REF.	DEBIT	CREDIT

Name ____

EXERCISE 12-17

EXERCISE 12-18

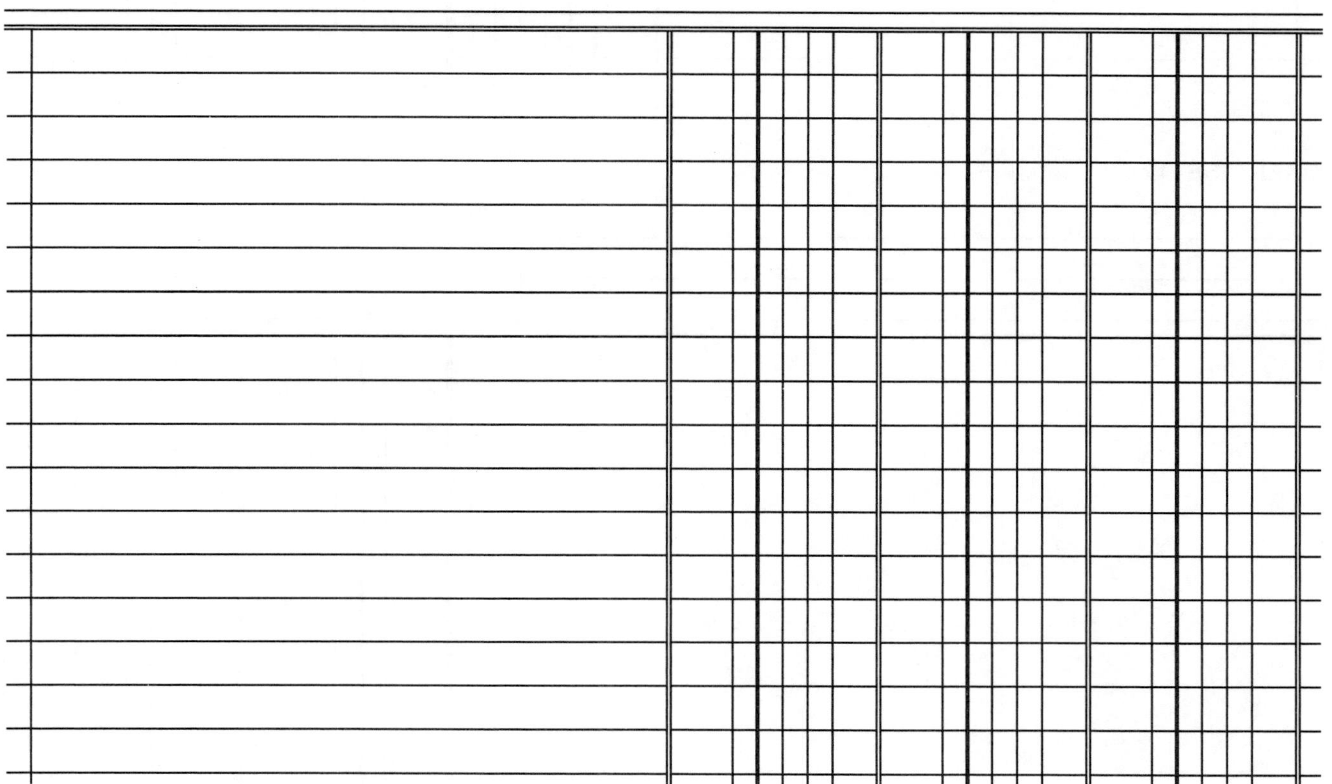

EXERCISE 12-19

EXERCISE 12-20

Name ______________________________________

EXERCISE 12-21

EXERCISE 12-22

EXERCISE 12-23

a.

b.

Name ______________________________

PROBLEM 12-1 ___

1.

Year	Total Dividends	Preferred Dividends		Common Dividends	
		Total	Per Share	Total	Per Share
2002					
2003					
2004					
2005					
2006					
2007					

Supporting calculations:

PROBLEM 12-1 ___, Concluded

2.

3.

PROBLEM 12-2 ___

JOURNAL

PAGE

DATE		DESCRIPTION	POST. REF.	DEBIT	CREDIT

PROBLEM 12-2 ___, Concluded

JOURNAL

PAGE

DATE		DESCRIPTION	POST. REF.	DEBIT	CREDIT

PROBLEM 12-3 ___

a.–g.

JOURNAL

PAGE

DATE		DESCRIPTION	POST. REF.	DEBIT	CREDIT

PROBLEM 12-3 ___, Concluded

JOURNAL

PAGE

DATE	DESCRIPTION	POST. REF.	DEBIT	CREDIT

Name ____

PROBLEM 12-4 ___

1. and 2.

Common Stock

Paid-In Capital in Excess of Stated Value

Retained Earnings

Treasury Stock

Paid-In Capital from Sale of Treasury Stock

PROBLEM 12-4 ___, Continued

Stock Dividends Distributable

Stock Dividends

Cash Dividends

PROBLEM 12-4 ___, Continued

2.

JOURNAL

PAGE

DATE		DESCRIPTION	POST. REF.	DEBIT	CREDIT

PROBLEM 12-4 ___, Concluded

3.

4.

Name ______________________________

PROBLEM 12-5 ___

JOURNAL

PAGE

DATE		DESCRIPTION	POST. REF.	DEBIT	CREDIT

PROBLEM 12-5 ___, Concluded

JOURNAL

PAGE

DATE		DESCRIPTION	POST. REF.	DEBIT	CREDIT

EXERCISE 13-1

	COMMON STOCK, $2 PAR	PAID-IN CAPITAL IN EXCESS OF PAR	TREASURY STOCK	RETAINED EARNINGS	TOTAL

EXERCISE 13-2

JOURNAL PAGE

	DATE		DESCRIPTION	POST. REF.	DEBIT	CREDIT	
1							1
2							2
3							3
4							4
5							5
6							6

EXERCISE 13-3

	Moore	**Knell**
a.		
b.		
c.		
d.		
e.		

Supporting calculations:

Name ______________________________

EXERCISE 13-4

	Moore	Knell
a.	________	________
b.	________	________
c.	________	________
d.	________	________
e.	________	________

Supporting calculations:

EXERCISE 13-5

EXERCISE 13-6

EXERCISE 13-7

a.

b. (1) and (2)

JOURNAL PAGE

	DATE		DESCRIPTION	POST. REF.	DEBIT	CREDIT	
1							1
2							2
3							3
4							4
5							5
6							6
7							7
8							8
9							9

Name ______________________

EXERCISE 13-8

a.

b.

JOURNAL PAGE

	DATE		DESCRIPTION	POST. REF.	DEBIT	CREDIT	
1							1
2							2
3							3
4							4
5							5
6							6
7							7
8							8
9							9
10							10
11							11
12							12

c. *Omit "00" in the cents columns.*

Statement of Members' Equity

EXERCISE 13-9

a.

JOURNAL PAGE

	DATE		DESCRIPTION	POST. REF.	DEBIT	CREDIT	
1							1
2							2
3							3
4							4
5							5
6							6
7							7
8							8
9							9
10							10
11							11
12							12

b. *Omit "00" in cents columns.*

Statement of Partnership Equity

EXERCISE 13-10

a. and b.

JOURNAL PAGE

	DATE		DESCRIPTION	POST. REF.	DEBIT	CREDIT	
1							1
2							2
3							3
4							4
5							5
6							6
7							7
8							8
9							9
10							10
11							11
12							12

EXERCISE 13-11

a. and b.

JOURNAL PAGE

	DATE		DESCRIPTION	POST. REF.	DEBIT	CREDIT	
1							1
2							2
3							3

EXERCISE 13-12

a.

b._

c. ______________________________

EXERCISE 13-13

a. (1) and (2)

JOURNAL PAGE

	DATE	DESCRIPTION	POST. REF.	DEBIT	CREDIT	
1						1
2						2
3						3
4						4
5						5
6						6
7						7
8						8

b.

EXERCISE 13-14

a.

JOURNAL PAGE

	DATE	DESCRIPTION	POST. REF.	DEBIT	CREDIT	
1						1
2						2
3						3
4						4
5						5
6						6
7						7
8						8

b.

Name ______________________________

EXERCISE 13-15

a. and b. (1) and (2)

JOURNAL PAGE

	DATE		DESCRIPTION	POST. REF.	DEBIT	CREDIT	
1							1
2							2
3							3
4							4
5							5
6							6
7							7
8							8
9							9
10							10
11							11
12							12
13							13

Supporting calculations:

EXERCISE 13-16

Omit "00" in the cents columns.

Statement of Partnership Equity

Supporting calculations:

Name ______________________________

EXERCISE 13-17

a. and b.

JOURNAL PAGE

	DATE		DESCRIPTION	POST. REF.	DEBIT	CREDIT	
1							1
2							2
3							3
4							4
5							5
6							6
7							7
8							8
9							9
10							10
11							11
12							12

EXERCISE 13-18

a. – f.

EXERCISE 13-18, Concluded

EXERCISE 13-19

a.

b. and c.

Name ______________________________

EXERCISE 13-20

EXERCISE 13-21

a. ______________________________

b.

c.

JOURNAL PAGE

	DATE		DESCRIPTION	POST. REF.	DEBIT	CREDIT	
1							1
2							2
3							3

Supporting calculations:

EXERCISE 13-22

a.

b.

EXERCISE 13-23

EXERCISE 13-24

Omit "00" in the cents columns.

Gibbs, Hill, and Manson

Statement of Partnership Liquidation

For the Period Ending July 1–29, 20--

	CASH	NONCASH ASSETS	LIABILITIES	CAPITAL		
				GIBBS	HILL	MANSION

EXERCISE 13-25

a. *Omit "00" in the cents columns.*

City Signs, LLC

Statement of LLC Liquidation

For the Period March 1–31, 2006

	CASH	NONCASH ASSETS	LIABILITIES	CAPITAL		
				ELLIS	ROANE	CLAUSEN

EXERCISE 13-25, Concluded

b.

JOURNAL

PAGE

	DATE		DESCRIPTION	POST. REF.	DEBIT	CREDIT	
1							1
2							2
3							3
4							4
5							5
6							6
7							7
8							8
9							9
10							10
11							11
12							12

Page not used.

PROBLEM 13-1___

1. and 3. **JOURNAL** PAGE

	DATE		DESCRIPTION	POST. REF.	DEBIT	CREDIT	
1							1
2							2
3							3
4							4
5							5
6							6
7							7
8							8
9							9
10							10
11							11
12							12
13							13
14							14
15							15
16							16
17							17
18							18
19							19
20							20
21							21
22							22
23							23
24							24
25							25
26							26
27							27
28							28
29							29
30							30
31							31
32							32
33							33
34							34
35							35
36							36
37							37

PROBLEM 13-1___, Concluded

PROBLEM 13-2___

	(1)		(2)	
	Net Income of		**Net Income of**	
Plan				
a.				
b.				
c.				
d.				
e.				
f.				

Supporting calculations:

PROBLEM 13-2___, Concluded

PROBLEM 13-3___, Concluded

3.

Page not used.

Name ______________________________

PROBLEM 13-4 ___

1. and 2.

JOURNAL

PAGE

DATE		DESCRIPTION	POST. REF.	DEBIT	CREDIT

PROBLEM 13-4___, Concluded

3. *Omit "00" in the cents columns.*

PROBLEM 13-5___

Omit "00" in the cents columns.

Statement of Partnership Liquidation

	CASH	NONCASH ASSETS	LIABILITIES	CAPITAL		

PROBLEM 13-5___, Concluded

2.

PROBLEM 13-6___

1. *Omit "00" in the cents columns.*

Statement of Partnership Liquidation

	CASH	NONCASH ASSETS	LIABILITIES	CAPITAL		

PROBLEM 13-6___, Continued

2. *Omit "00" in the cents columns.*

Statement of Partnership Liquidation

	CASH	NONCASH ASSETS	LIABILITIES	CAPITAL		

EXERCISE 14-1

JOURNAL PAGE

DATE		DESCRIPTION	POST. REF.	DEBIT	CREDIT

EXERCISE 14-2

JOURNAL PAGE

DATE		DESCRIPTION	POST. REF.	DEBIT	CREDIT

EXERCISE 14-3

a.

b.

JOURNAL PAGE

	DATE		DESCRIPTION	POST. REF.	DEBIT	CREDIT	
1							1
2							2
3							3
4							4
5							5

c.

Name ______________________________

EXERCISE 14-4

a.

JOURNAL PAGE

	DATE		DESCRIPTION	POST. REF.	DEBIT	CREDIT	
1							1
2							2
3							3
4							4
5							5
6							6

b.

EXERCISE 14-5

a. and b.

JOURNAL PAGE

	DATE		DESCRIPTION	POST. REF.	DEBIT	CREDIT	
1							1
2							2
3							3
4							4
5							5
6							6
7							7
8							8

EXERCISE 14-5, Concluded

c. Balance sheet disclosure:

Note disclosure:

EXERCISE 14-6

a.

EXERCISE 14-6, Concluded

b. and c.

JOURNAL

PAGE

	DATE		DESCRIPTION	POST. REF.	DEBIT	CREDIT	
1							1
2							2
3							3
4							4
5							5
6							6

d. Balance sheet disclosure:

e. Note disclosure:

EXERCISE 14-7

a. and c.

JOURNAL PAGE

	DATE		DESCRIPTION	POST. REF.	DEBIT	CREDIT	
1							1
2							2
3							3
4							4
5							5
6							6
7							7
8							8
9							9

b. Balance sheet disclosure:

Note disclosure:

Name ______________________________

EXERCISE 14-8

a. and b.

JOURNAL PAGE

	DATE		DESCRIPTION	POST. REF.	DEBIT	CREDIT	
1							1
2							2
3							3
4							4
5							5
6							6

c. Balance sheet disclosure:

EXERCISE 14-9

EXERCISE 14-10

EXERCISE 14-11

a. ______________________ e. ______________________

b. ______________________ f. ______________________

c. ______________________ g. ______________________

d. ______________________ h. ______________________

EXERCISE 14-12

Name ______________________________

EXERCISE 14-13

EXERCISE 14-14

EXERCISE 14-15

a. – c.

EXERCISE 14-16

a. ____________ **e.** ____________

b. ____________ **f.** ____________

c. ____________ **g.** ____________

d. ____________ **h.** ____________

EXERCISE 14-17

a.

b.

EXERCISE 14-18

a.– c.

EXERCISE 14-19

a. and b.

JOURNAL PAGE

	DATE		DESCRIPTION	POST. REF.	DEBIT	CREDIT	
1							1
2							2
3							3
4							4
5							5
6							6
7							7
8							8

EXERCISE 14-20

a.

EXERCISE 14-20, Concluded

b.

EXERCISE 14-21

a.–c.

JOURNAL PAGE

DATE		DESCRIPTION	POST. REF.	DEBIT	CREDIT

EXERCISE 14-22

a. and b.

JOURNAL PAGE

	DATE		DESCRIPTION	POST. REF.	DEBIT	CREDIT	
1							1
2							2
3							3
4							4
5							5
6							6
7							7

EXERCISE 14-23

a. and b.

EXERCISE 14-24

a. (1) and (2)

b.

EXERCISE 14-25

a. and b.

EXERCISE 14-25, Concluded

c.

EXERCISE 14-26

a.

b.

PROBLEM 14-1 ___

1. and 2.

Year	**Income Tax Deducted on Income Statement**	**Income Tax Payments for the Year**	**Deferred Income Tax Payable**	
			Year's Addition (Deduction)	**Year-End Balance**
First				
Second				
Third				
Fourth				
Total				

Page not used.

Name ____

PROBLEM 14-2 ___

Omit "00" in the cents columns.

PROBLEM 14-2 ___, Concluded

Name ______________________

PROBLEM 14-3 ___

1.

PROBLEM 14-3 ___, Continued

2.

PROBLEM 14-3 ___, Continued

3.

PROBLEM 14-3 ___, Concluded

PROBLEM 14-4 ___

JOURNAL PAGE

DATE		DESCRIPTION	POST. REF.	DEBIT	CREDIT

PROBLEM 14-4 ___, Concluded

JOURNAL

PAGE

DATE	DESCRIPTION	POST. REF.	DEBIT	CREDIT

EXERCISE 15-1

	(a)	(b)	(c)
Earnings before bond interest and income tax	$1,600,000	$2,400,000	$4,000,000
Bond interest			
Balance			
Income tax			
Net income			
Dividends on preferred stock			
Earnings available for common stock			
Earnings per share on common stock			

EXERCISE 15-2

EXERCISE 15-3

EXERCISE 15-4

a. ______________________________

____

____

____

____

b.

EXERCISE 15-5

a. ______________________________

____

____

____

____

____

b.

EXERCISE 15-6

____

____

EXERCISE 15-7

____

____

____

____

____

____

____

____

____

____

____

Name ______________________

EXERCISE 15-8

EXERCISE 15-9

EXERCISE 15-10

EXERCISE 15-11

JOURNAL PAGE

DATE	DESCRIPTION	POST. REF.	DEBIT	CREDIT

EXERCISE 15-12

a. 1.–4.

JOURNAL PAGE

DATE	DESCRIPTION	POST. REF.	DEBIT	CREDIT

b.

EXERCISE 15-12, Concluded

Supporting calculations:

EXERCISE 15-13

a. and b.

JOURNAL PAGE

	DATE		DESCRIPTION	POST. REF.	DEBIT	CREDIT	
1							1
2							2
3							3
4							4
5							5
6							6
7							7

Supporting calculations:

EXERCISE 15-14

JOURNAL

PAGE

DATE		DESCRIPTION	POST. REF.	DEBIT	CREDIT

EXERCISE 15-15

JOURNAL

PAGE

DATE		DESCRIPTION	POST. REF.	DEBIT	CREDIT

EXERCISE 15-16

EXERCISE 15-17

EXERCISE 15-18

a.–d.

JOURNAL PAGE

DATE		DESCRIPTION	POST. REF.	DEBIT	CREDIT

EXERCISE 15-19

a.–d.

JOURNAL PAGE

	DATE		DESCRIPTION	POST. REF.	DEBIT	CREDIT	
1							1
2							2
3							3
4							4
5							5
6							6
7							7
8							8
9							9
10							10
11							11
12							12
13							13
14							14
15							15
16							16
17							17

EXERCISE 15-20

a. Current year: ______________________________

Preceding year: ______________________________

b. ______________________________

Name ______________________________

APPENDIX EXERCISE 15-21

a. 1.–4.

JOURNAL

PAGE

	DATE		DESCRIPTION	POST. REF.	DEBIT	CREDIT	
1							1
2							2
3							3
4							4
5							5
6							6
7							7
8							8
9							9
10							10
11							11
12							12
13							13

Supporting calculations:

b.

APPENDIX EXERCISE 15-22

a. 1.–3.

JOURNAL

PAGE

	DATE		DESCRIPTION	POST. REF.	DEBIT	CREDIT	
1							1
2							2
3							3
4							4
5							5
6							6
7							7
8							8
9							9
10							10
11							11
12							12
13							13
14							14
15							15

Supporting calculations:

b.

APPENDIX EXERCISE 15-23

a.–d.

APPENDIX EXERCISE 15-24

a.–d.

Name ______________________________

PROBLEM 15-1 ___

1.

	Plan 1	*Plan 2*	*Plan 3*
Earnings before interest and income tax			
Deduct interest on bonds			
Income before income tax			
Deduct income tax			
Net income			
Dividends on preferred stock			
Available for dividends on common stock			
Shares of common stock outstanding			
Earnings per share on common stock			

2.

	Plan 1	*Plan 2*	*Plan 3*
Earnings before interest and income tax			
Deduct interest on bonds			
Income before income tax			
Deduct income tax			
Net income			
Dividends on preferred stock			
Available for dividends on common stock			
Shares of common stock outstanding			
Earnings per share on common stock			

PROBLEM 15-1 ___, Concluded

3.

Name ____________________

PROBLEM 15-2 ___

1. and 2.

JOURNAL

PAGE

	DATE		DESCRIPTION	POST. REF.	DEBIT	CREDIT	
1							1
2							2
3							3
4							4
5							5
6							6
7							7
8							8
9							9
10							10
11							11
12							12
13							13
14							14
15							15
16							16
17							17
18							18
19							19
20							20
21							21
22							22
23							23
24							24
25							25
26							26
27							27
28							28
29							29
30							30
31							31
32							32
33							33
34							34
35							35
36							36

PROBLEM 15-2 ___, Concluded

JOURNAL

PAGE

DATE		DESCRIPTION	POST. REF.	DEBIT	CREDIT

3.

4.

Name ______________________________

PROBLEM 15-3 ___

1. and 2.

JOURNAL

PAGE

DATE		DESCRIPTION	POST. REF.	DEBIT	CREDIT

PROBLEM 15-3 ___, Concluded

JOURNAL

PAGE

	DATE		DESCRIPTION	POST. REF.	DEBIT	CREDIT	
1							1
2							2
3							3
4							4
5							5
6							6
7							7
8							8
9							9
10							10
11							11
12							12
13							13
14							14
15							15
16							16
17							17
18							18
19							19

3.

4.

PROBLEM 15-4 ___

1.

JOURNAL

PAGE

DATE		DESCRIPTION	POST. REF.	DEBIT	CREDIT

PROBLEM 15-4 ___, Concluded

JOURNAL

PAGE

DATE		DESCRIPTION	POST. REF.	DEBIT	CREDIT

2. (a) 2005: ______________________________

(b) 2006: ______________________________

3.

PROBLEM 15-5 ___

JOURNAL

PAGE

DATE		DESCRIPTION	POST. REF.	DEBIT	CREDIT

PROBLEM 15-5 ___, Concluded

JOURNAL

PAGE

DATE		DESCRIPTION	POST. REF.	DEBIT	CREDIT

Name ______________________________

APPENDIX PROBLEM 15-6 ___

1. a. and b.

JOURNAL PAGE

	DATE		DESCRIPTION	POST. REF.	DEBIT	CREDIT	
1							1
2							2
3							3
4							4
5							5
6							6
7							7
8							8
9							9
10							10
11							11
12							12
13							13
14							14
15							15
16							16
17							17
18							18
19							19

2.

APPENDIX PROBLEM 15-7 ___

1. a. and b.

JOURNAL

PAGE

	DATE		DESCRIPTION	POST. REF.	DEBIT	CREDIT	
1							1
2							2
3							3
4							4
5							5
6							6
7							7
8							8
9							9
10							10
11							11
12							12
13							13
14							14
15							15
16							16
17							17
18							18
19							19

2.

Name ____________________________________

COMPREHENSIVE PROBLEM 4

1.

JOURNAL

PAGE

DATE		DESCRIPTION	POST. REF.	DEBIT	CREDIT

COMPREHENSIVE PROBLEM 4, Continued

JOURNAL

PAGE

DATE		DESCRIPTION	POST. REF.	DEBIT	CREDIT

COMPREHENSIVE PROBLEM 4, Continued

2. a. *Omit "00" in the cents columns.*

Income Statement

COMPREHENSIVE PROBLEM 4, Continued

Income Statement (Concluded)

COMPREHENSIVE PROBLEM 4, Continued

2. b. *Omit "00" in the cents columns.*

Retained Earnings Statement

COMPREHENSIVE PROBLEM 4, Continued

2. c. *Omit "00" in the cents columns.*

Balance Sheet

COMPREHENSIVE PROBLEM 4, Concluded

Balance Sheet (Concluded)

Page not used.

Name ______________________________

EXERCISE 16-1

____
____
____
____
____
____
____
____
____
____
____
____
____

EXERCISE 16-2

a. ______________________________
b. ______________________________
c. ______________________________
d. ______________________________
e. ______________________________
f. ______________________________
g. ______________________________
h. ______________________________

EXERCISE 16-3

a. Purchased patents: ______________________________
b. Purchased buildings: ______________________________
c. Purchased treasury stock: ______________________________
d. Sold equipment: ______________________________
e. Net income: ______________________________
f. Issued preferred stock: ______________________________
g. Redeemed bonds: ______________________________
h. Paid cash dividends: ______________________________
i. Sold long-term investments: ______________________________
j. Issued common stock: ______________________________
k. Issued bonds: ______________________________

EXERCISE 16-4

a. Increase in notes payable due in 90 days to vendors: ______

b. Loss on disposal of fixed assets: ______

c. Decrease in accounts payable: ______

d. Increase in notes receivable due in 90 days from customers: ______

e. Decrease in salaries payable: ______

f. Decrease in prepaid expenses: ______

g. Depreciation of fixed assets: ______

h. Decrease in accounts receivable: ______

i. Amortization of patent: ______

j. Increase in merchandise inventory: ______

k. Gain on retirement of long-term debt: ______

EXERCISE 16-5

a.

b. ______

EXERCISE 16-6

EXERCISE 16-7

EXERCISE 16-8

EXERCISE 16-9

EXERCISE 16-10

EXERCISE 16-11

Name ______________________

EXERCISE 16-12

EXERCISE 16-13

EXERCISE 16-14

EXERCISE 16-15

EXERCISE 16-16

a.

b.

Name ______________________

EXERCISE 16-17

EXERCISE 16-18

a.

b.

EXERCISE 16-19

Name ______________________________

EXERCISE 16-20

EXERCISE 16-21

EXERCISE 16-22

EXERCISE 16-23

EXERCISE 16-24

a. and b.

	FISCAL YEARS ENDED	
	2003	2002

c.

Name ____________________

PROBLEM 16-1 ___

Omit "00" in the cents columns.

PROBLEM 16-1 ___, Continued

PROBLEM 16-1 ___, Continued

The use of this form is not required unless so indicated by the instructor.

Work Sheet for Statement of Cash Flows

ACCOUNTS	BALANCE, ________, 2005	TRANSACTIONS		BALANCE, ________, 2006
		DEBIT	CREDIT	

PROBLEM 16-1 ___, Concluded

ACCOUNTS	BALANCE, ________, 2005	TRANSACTIONS		BALANCE, ________, 2006
		DEBIT	CREDIT	

Name ____

PROBLEM 16-2 ___

Omit "00" in the cents columns.

PROBLEM 16-2 ___, Continued

Name ____________________

PROBLEM 16-2 ___, Continued

The use of this form is not required unless so indicated by the instructor.

Work Sheet for Statement of Cash Flows

ACCOUNTS	BALANCE, DEC. 31, 2005	TRANSACTIONS		BALANCE, DEC. 31, 2006
		DEBIT	CREDIT	

PROBLEM 16-2 ___, Concluded

ACCOUNTS	BALANCE, DEC. 31, 2005	TRANSACTIONS		BALANCE, DEC. 31, 2006
		DEBIT	CREDIT	

PROBLEM 16-3 ___

Omit "00" in the cents columns.

PROBLEM 16-3 ___, Continued

PROBLEM 16-3 ___, Continued

The use of this form is not required unless so indicated by the instructor.

Work Sheet for Statement of Cash Flows

ACCOUNTS	BALANCE, DEC. 31, 2005	TRANSACTIONS		BALANCE, DEC. 31, 2006
		DEBIT	CREDIT	

PROBLEM 16-3 ___, Concluded

ACCOUNTS	BALANCE, DEC. 31, 2005	TRANSACTIONS		BALANCE, DEC. 31, 2006
		DEBIT	CREDIT	

PROBLEM 16-4 ___

Omit "00" in the cents columns.

PROBLEM 16-4 ___, Continued

PROBLEM 16-4 ___, Continued

The use of this form is not required unless so indicated by the instructor.

Work Sheet for Statement of Cash Flows

ACCOUNTS	BALANCE, DEC. 31, 2006	TRANSACTIONS		BALANCE, DEC. 31, 2007
		DEBIT	CREDIT	

PROBLEM 16-4 ___, Concluded

ACCOUNTS	BALANCE, DEC. 31, 2006	TRANSACTIONS		BALANCE, DEC. 31, 2007
		DEBIT	CREDIT	

Name ______________________________

PROBLEM 16-5 ___

Omit "00" in the cents columns.

PROBLEM 16-5 ___, Continued

PROBLEM 16-5 ___, Continued

The use of this form is not required unless so indicated by the instructor.

Work Sheet for Statement of Cash Flows

ACCOUNTS	BALANCE, ________, 2005	TRANSACTIONS DEBIT	TRANSACTIONS CREDIT	BALANCE, ________, 2006

PROBLEM 16-5 ___, Concluded

ACCOUNTS	BALANCE, ________, 2005	TRANSACTIONS DEBIT	TRANSACTIONS CREDIT	BALANCE, ________, 2006

EXERCISE 17-1

a.

	2006		2005	
	AMOUNT	PERCENT	AMOUNT	PERCENT

b.

EXERCISE 17-2

a.

	FISCAL YEAR 2002		FISCAL YEAR 2001	
	AMOUNT	PERCENT	AMOUNT	PERCENT

b.

Name ______________________

EXERCISE 17-3

a.

	HORIZON PUBLISHING COMPANY		PUBLISHING INDUSTRY AVERAGE
	AMOUNT	PERCENT	PERCENT

b.

EXERCISE 17-4

	2006		2005	
	AMOUNT	PERCENT	AMOUNT	PERCENT

EXERCISE 17-5

a.

	2006	2005	INCREASE (DECREASE)	
	AMOUNT	AMOUNT	AMOUNT	PERCENT

b.

Name ____________________

EXERCISE 17-6

a. (1)

(2)

(3)

b.

EXERCISE 17-7

a. (1)

(2)

b.

Name ______________________________

EXERCISE 17-8

a. ______________________________

b. ______________________________

EXERCISE 17-9

a. (1)

(2)

b.

Name ______________________________

EXERCISE 17-10

a. (1)

(2)

b.

EXERCISE 17-11

a. (1)

(2)

b.

Name ______________________________

EXERCISE 17-12

a. (1) ______________________________

(2) ______________________________

b. ______________________________

EXERCISE 17-13

a.

b.

c.

EXERCISE 17-14

a.

b.

c.

EXERCISE 17-15

a.

b.

c.

Name ______________________________

EXERCISE 17-16

a. ______________________________

b._

EXERCISE 17-17

a.

b.

Name ______________________________

EXERCISE 17-18

a. ______________________________

b. ______________________________

c. ______________________________

d. ______________________________

EXERCISE 17-19

a.

b.

c.

d.

e.

f.

Name ______________________________

EXERCISE 17-20

a. ______________________________

b. ______________________________

c. ______________________________

d. ______________________________

e. ______________________________

f. ______________________________

EXERCISE 17-21

a.

b.

c.

d.

Name ____________________

EXERCISE 17-22

a.

b.

EXERCISE 17-23

a.

b.

Name ______________________________

PROBLEM 17-1 ___

1.

Comparative Income Statement

	2006	2005	INCREASE (DECREASE)	
			AMOUNT	PERCENT

PROBLEM 17-1 ___, Concluded

2.

Name ______________________________________

PROBLEM 17-2 ___

1.

Comparative Income Statement

	2006		2005	
	AMOUNT	PERCENT	AMOUNT	PERCENT

PROBLEM 17-2 ___, Concluded

2.

Name ______________________________

PROBLEM 17-3 ___

1. a. ______________________________

b. ______________________________

c. ______________________________

PROBLEM 17-3 ___, Concluded

2.

Transaction	Working Capital	Current Ratio	Quick Ratio
a.			
b.			
c.			
d.			
e.			
f.			
g.			
h.			
i.			
j.			

Supporting calculations:

PROBLEM 17-4 ___

1. through 19.

PROBLEM 17-4 ___, Concluded

Name ______________________________

PROBLEM 17-5 ___

1. a.

Rate earned on total assets

Year

PROBLEM 17-5 ___, Continued

1. b.

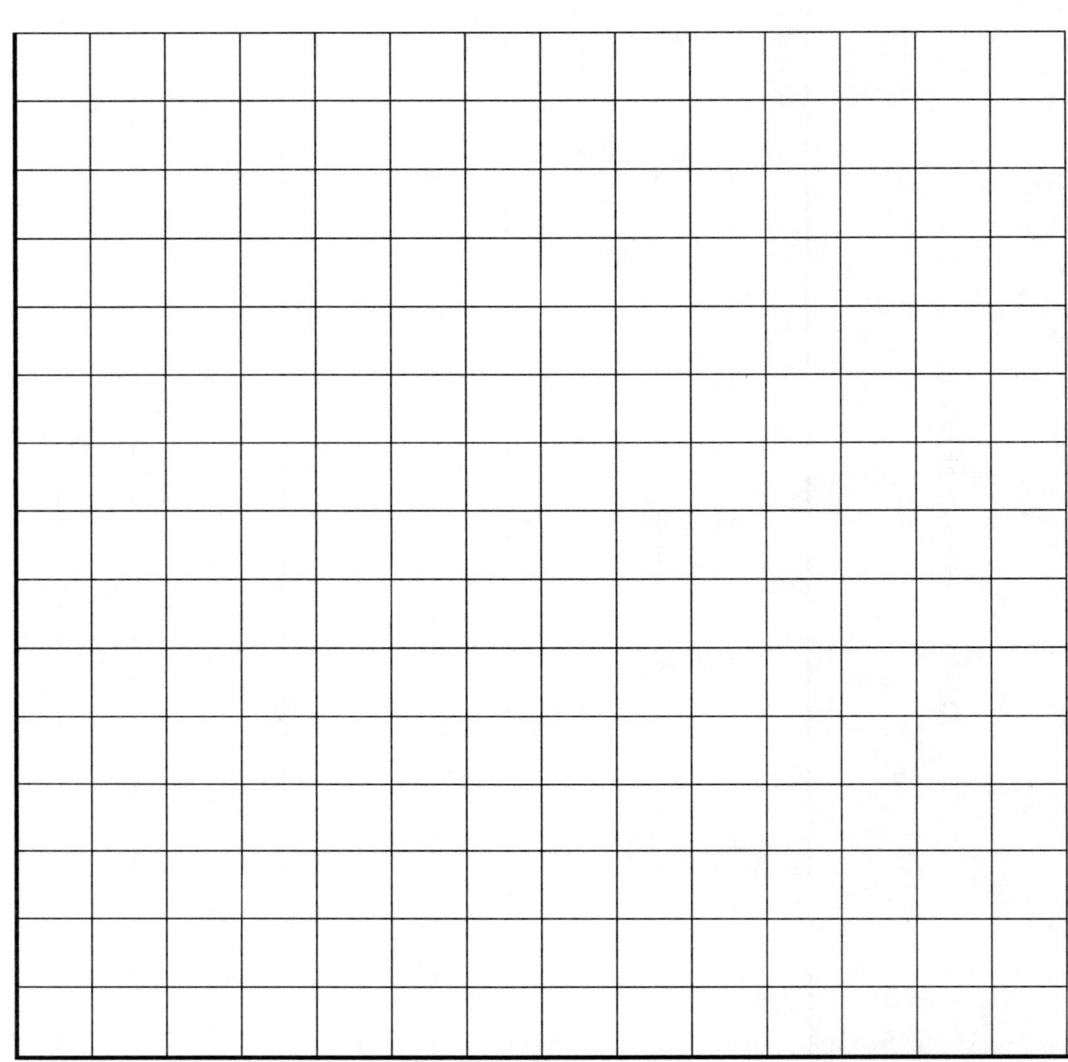

PROBLEM 17-5 ___, Continued

1. c.

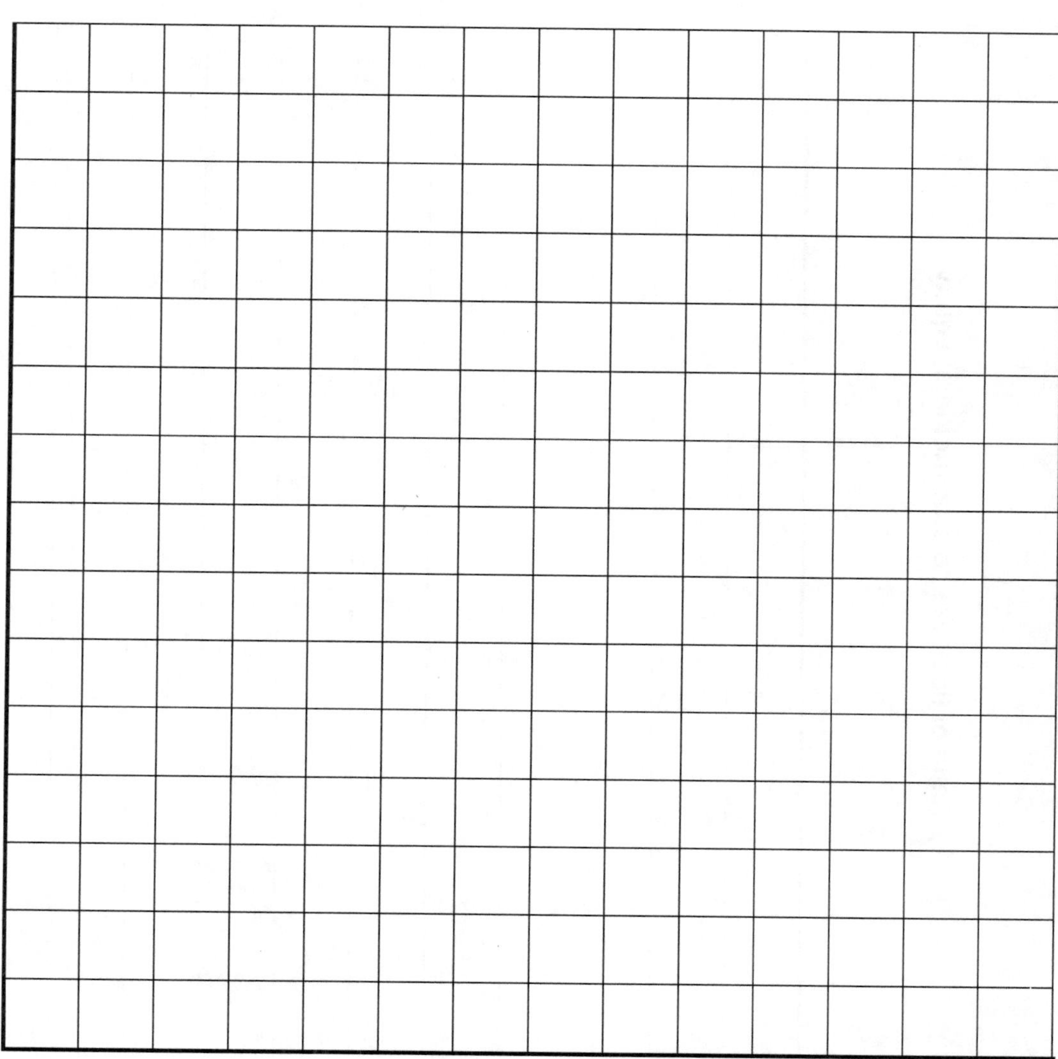

PROBLEM 17-5 ___, Continued

1. d.

Ratio of liabilities to stockholders' equity

Year

PROBLEM 17-5 ___, Continued

2.

PROBLEM 17-5 ___, Concluded

Name ____________________

HOME DEPOT, INC., PROBLEM

1. a. through m.

HOME DEPOT, INC., PROBLEM, Continued

HOME DEPOT, INC., PROBLEM, Continued

2. a. through m.

HOME DEPOT, INC., PROBLEM, Concluded

Name ______________________________

EXERCISE 18-1

a. Inspector salaries: ______________________________

b. Depreciation on woodworking machinery: ______________________________

c. Assembly wages: ______________________________

d. Wood: ______________________________

e. Wages of wood cutters: ______________________________

f. Furniture hardware: ______________________________

g. Saw blades: ______________________________

h. Supervisor salaries: ______________________________

EXERCISE 18-2

a. Depreciation on the St. Bernard (Cincinnati) soap plant: ______________________________

b. Wages paid to Packing Department employees: ______________________________

c. Maintenance supplies: ______________________________

d. Packaging materials: ______________________________

e. Plant manager salary of the Lima, Ohio, liquid soap plant: ______________________________

f. Pulp for towel and tissue products: ______________________________

g. Wages of Making Department employees: ______________________________

h. Scents and fragrances: ______________________________

i. Depreciation on disposable diaper converting machines: ______________________________

j. Salary of process engineers: ______________________________

EXERCISE 18-3

a. Plant manager's salary at Greeneville, Tennessee, turf care products plant: ______________________________

b. Depreciation on Moline, Illinois, headquarters building: ______________________________

c. Property taxes on Klemme, Iowa, components plant: ______________________________

d. Chief financial officer's salary: ______________________________

e. Steel plate: ______________________________

f. Sales incentive fees to dealers: ______________________________

g. Amortization of patents on a new welding process: ______________________________

h. Interest expense on debt: ______________________________

i. Consultant fees for surveying production employee morale: ______________________________

j. Factory supplies used in the Kenersville, North Carolina, hydraulic excavator factory: ______________________________

EXERCISE 18-4

a. Advertising: ______

b. Tires: ______

c. Assembly employee wages: ______

d. Salary of marketing executive: ______

e. Depreciation of Dearborn, Michigan, executive building: ______

f. CEO's salary: ______

g. Plant manager's salary: ______

h. Depreciation on Atlanta, Georgia, assembly plant: ______

i. Maintenance supplies: ______

j. Glass: ______

k. Property taxes on Kansas City, Missouri, assembly plant: ______

l. Shipping costs: ______

m. Travel costs used by sales personnel: ______

n. Utility costs used in executive building: ______

o. Stamping Department employee wages: ______

p. Steel: ______

EXERCISE 18-5

a. ______

b. ______

c. ______

d. ______

e. ______

f. ______

g. ______

h. ______

EXERCISE 18-6

a. ______

b. ______

c. ______

d. ______

e. ______

EXERCISE 18-7

a. Cost of goods sold: ______

EXERCISE 18-7, Concluded

b. Direct materials cost: ______________________

c. Direct labor cost: ______________________

EXERCISE 18-8

a.

RECEIVED			ISSUED			BALANCE			
Receiving Report Number	**Quantity**	**Unit Price**	**Materials Requisition Number**	**Quantity**	**Amount**	**Date**	**Quantity**	**Amount**	**Unit Price**
						May 1	120	$2,160	$18.00
23	190	$20.00				May 3	____	____	____
							____	____	____
			104	250	____	May 5	____	____	____
29	140	22.00				May 19	____	____	____
							____	____	____
			117	160	____	May 25	____	____	____

b. ______________________

c. **JOURNAL** PAGE

	DATE		DESCRIPTION	POST. REF.	DEBIT	CREDIT	
1							1
2							2
3							3

d.

EXERCISE 18-9

JOURNAL PAGE

	DATE		DESCRIPTION	POST. REF.	DEBIT	CREDIT	
1							1
2							2
3							3
4							4
5							5

EXERCISE 18-10

a. and b.

JOURNAL PAGE

	DATE		DESCRIPTION	POST. REF.	DEBIT	CREDIT	
1							1
2							2
3							3
4							4
5							5
6							6
7							7
8							8

c.

EXERCISE 18-11

JOURNAL PAGE

	DATE		DESCRIPTION	POST. REF.	DEBIT	CREDIT	
1							1
2							2
3							3
4							4

EXERCISE 18-12

a.

JOURNAL PAGE

	DATE		DESCRIPTION	POST. REF.	DEBIT	CREDIT	
1							1
2							2
3							3
4							4

b.

EXERCISE 18-13

a. and b.

JOURNAL PAGE

	DATE		DESCRIPTION	POST. REF.	DEBIT	CREDIT	
1							1
2							2
3							3
4							4
5							5
6							6
7							7

EXERCISE 18-14

a. Factory 1 overhead rate: ______________________________

b. Factory 2 overhead rate: ______________________________

c. **JOURNAL** PAGE

	DATE		DESCRIPTION	POST. REF.	DEBIT	CREDIT	
1							1
2							2
3							3
4							4
5							5
6							6
7							7
8							8

d. Balance of Factory 1 accounts as of April 30: ______________________________

Balance of Factory 2 accounts as of April 30: ______________________________

EXERCISE 18-15

EXERCISE 18-16

a.

b.

c.

EXERCISE 18-17

a.

JOURNAL PAGE

	DATE		DESCRIPTION	POST. REF.	DEBIT	CREDIT	
1							1
2							2
3							3
4							4

b.

EXERCISE 18-18

a.–d.

JOURNAL PAGE

DATE		DESCRIPTION	POST. REF.	DEBIT	CREDIT

EXERCISE 18-19

a.

EXERCISE 18-19, Concluded

b.

Materials inventory:

Work in process inventory:

Finished goods inventory:

EXERCISE 18-20

a.

Date	Job No.	Quantity	Product	Amount	Unit Cost
Jan. 1	1	400	XXY	$ 7,600	_______
Jan. 29	26	1,200	AAB	18,000	_______
Feb. 15	43	600	AAB	9,600	_______
Mar. 10	64	450	XXY	7,650	_______
Mar. 31	75	900	MM	7,200	_______
May 10	91	1,000	MM	12,000	_______
June 20	104	400	XXY	4,800	_______
Aug. 2	112	1,500	MM	24,000	_______
Sept. 20	114	400	AAB	6,000	_______
Nov. 1	126	600	XXY	6,000	_______
Dec. 3	133	850	MM	17,850	_______

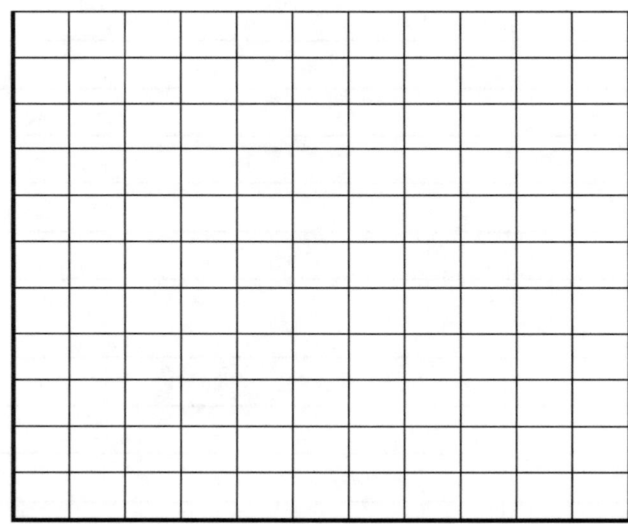

EXERCISE 18-19, Continued

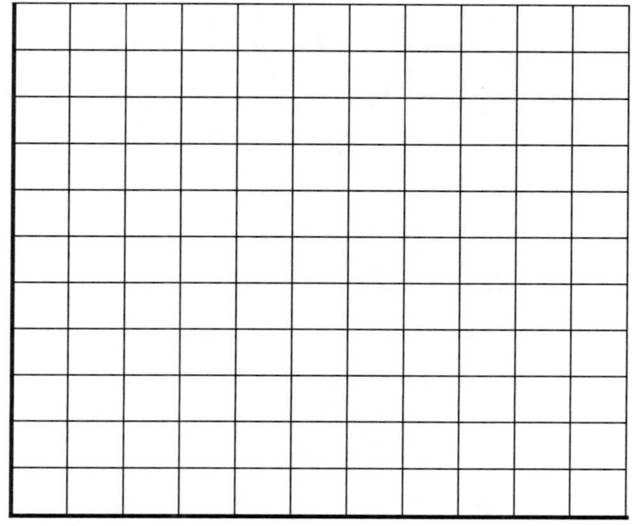

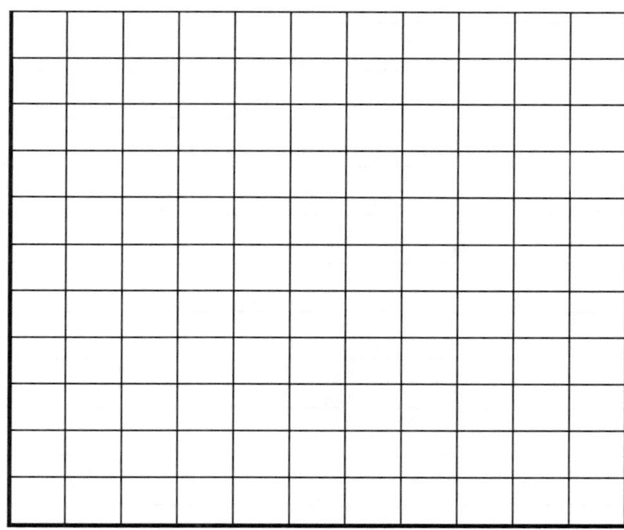

Cost performance over time for the three products:

____

____

____

____

____

EXERCISE 18-20, Concluded

b.

EXERCISE 18-21

a. and b.

EXERCISE 18-22

a.

JOURNAL

PAGE

DATE		DESCRIPTION	POST. REF.	DEBIT	CREDIT

b.

EXERCISE 18-22, Concluded

c.

EXERCISE 18-23

a.–d.

JOURNAL PAGE

DATE		DESCRIPTION	POST. REF.	DEBIT	CREDIT

Supporting calculations:

Name ______________________________

PROBLEM 18-1 ___

Cost	Product Costs			Period Costs	
	Direct Materials Cost	Direct Labor Cost	Factory Overhead Cost	Selling Expense	Administrative Expense
a.					
b.					
c.					
d.					
e.					
f.					
g.					
h.					
i.					
j.					
k.					
l.					
m.					
n.					
o.					
p.					
q.					
r.					
s.					
t.					
u.					
v.					
w.					
x.					
y.					
z.					

Page not used.

PROBLEM 18-2 ___

a.–i.

JOURNAL

PAGE

DATE		DESCRIPTION	POST. REF.	DEBIT	CREDIT

PROBLEM 18-2 ___, Concluded

JOURNAL

PAGE

DATE		DESCRIPTION	POST. REF.	DEBIT	CREDIT

PROBLEM 18-3 ___

1. a.–g.

JOURNAL

PAGE

DATE		DESCRIPTION	POST. REF.	DEBIT	CREDIT

PROBLEM 18-3 ___, Concluded

2.

Work in Process

Finished Goods

3.

Schedule of Unfinished Jobs

JOB	DIRECT MATERIALS	DIRECT LABOR	FACTORY OVERHEAD	TOTAL

4.

Schedule of Completed Jobs

	DIRECT MATERIALS	DIRECT LABOR	FACTORY OVERHEAD	TOTAL

Name ______________________________

PROBLEM 18-4 ___

1. and 2.

JOB ORDER COST SHEET

Customer ______________________ Date ______________________

Address ______________________ Date wanted ______________________

______________________ Date completed ______________________

Item ______________________ Job No. ______________________

ESTIMATE

Direct Materials		**Direct Labor**		**Summary**	
	Amount		Amount		Amount
___ meters at $ _____	______	___ hours at $ _____	______	Direct materials	______
___ meters at _____	______	___ hours at _____	______	Direct labor	______
___ meters at _____	______	___ hours at _____	______	Factory overhead	______
___ meters at _____	______	___ hours at _____	______		
Total	______	Total	______	Total cost	______

ACTUAL

Direct Materials			**Direct Labor**			**Summary**	
Mat. Req. No.	Description	Amount	Time Ticket No.	Description	Amount	Item	Amount
____	______	______	____	______	______	Direct materials	______
____	______	______	____	______	______	Direct labor	______
____	______	______	____	______	______	Factory overhead	______
____	______	______	____	______	______		
Total		______	Total		______	Total cost	______

Comments:

Page not used.

PROBLEM 18-5 ___

1. Supporting calculations:

Job No.	Quan-tity	Work in Process	Direct Materials	Direct Labor	Factory Overhead	Total Cost	Unit Cost	Units Sold	Cost of Goods Sold

(A) ____________________

(B) ____________________

(C) ____________________

(D) ____________________

(E) ____________________

(F) ____________________

(G) ____________________

(H) ____________________

PROBLEM 18-5 ___, Concluded

2.

PROBLEM 18-6 ___

1. *Omit "00" in the cents columns.*

Supporting calculations:

PROBLEM 18-6 ___, Concluded

2.

Name ______________________________

EXERCISE 19-1

a.–e.

JOURNAL

PAGE

DATE	DESCRIPTION	POST. REF.	DEBIT	CREDIT

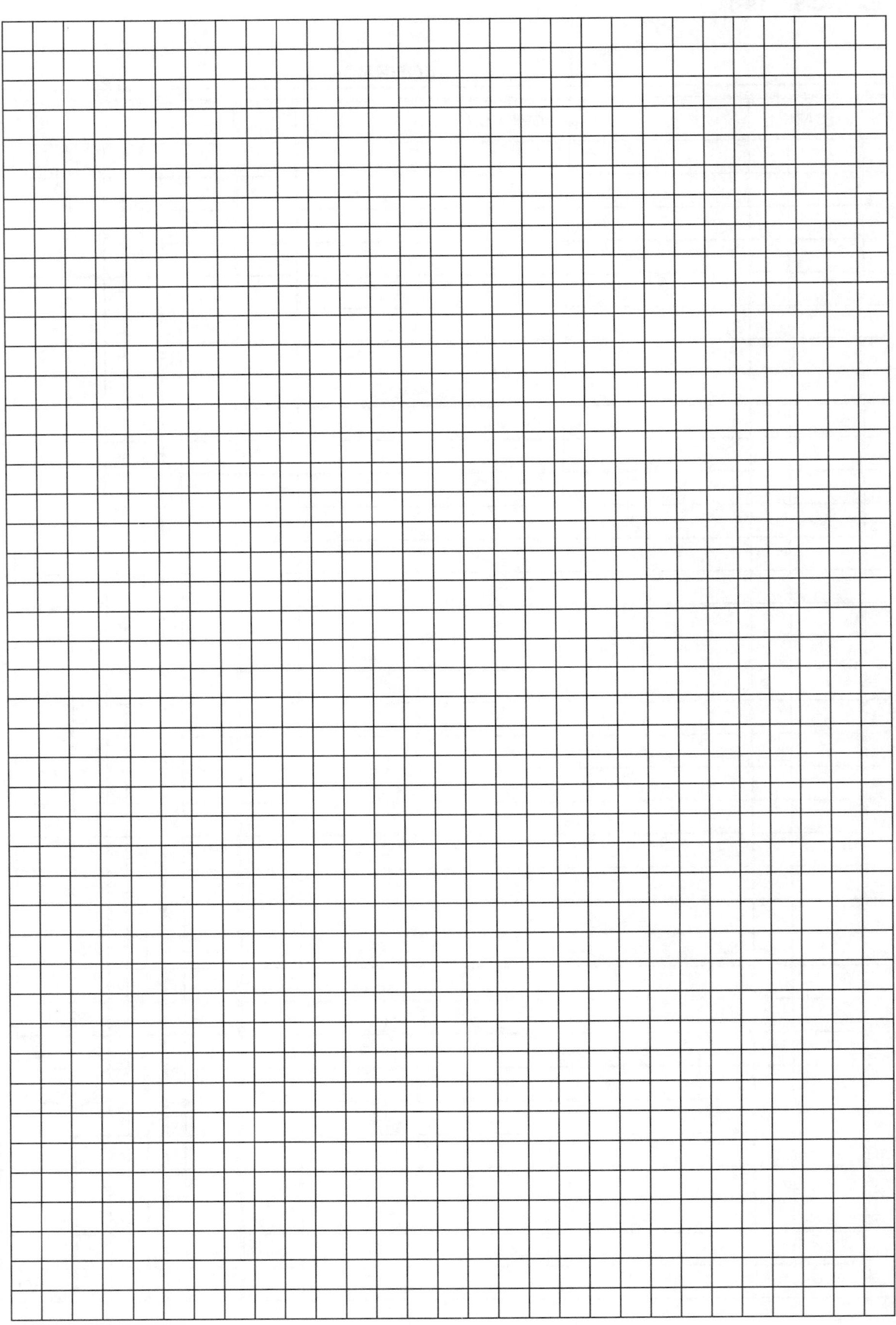

EXERCISE 19-2

EXERCISE 19-3

a.–b.

JOURNAL PAGE

	DATE	DESCRIPTION	POST. REF.	DEBIT	CREDIT	
1						1
2						2
3						3
4						4
5						5
6						6
7						7
8						8
9						9
10						10
11						11
12						12
13						13

EXERCISE 19-4

a. ______________________________

____

b.

JOURNAL PAGE

	DATE	DESCRIPTION	POST. REF.	DEBIT	CREDIT	
1						1
2						2
3						3
4						4
5						5
6						6

c.

d.

EXERCISE 19-5

UNITS	WHOLE UNITS	EQUIVALENT UNITS	
		DIRECT MATERIALS	CONVERSION

EXERCISE 19-6

a. Drawing Department

UNITS	WHOLE UNITS	EQUIVALENT UNITS	
		DIRECT MATERIALS	CONVERSION

EXERCISE 19-6, Concluded

b. Winding Department

UNITS	WHOLE UNITS	EQUIVALENT UNITS	
		DIRECT MATERIALS	CONVERSION

EXERCISE 19-7

a.

b.

UNITS	WHOLE UNITS	EQUIVALENT UNITS	
		DIRECT MATERIALS	CONVERSION

EXERCISE 19-8

a.

b.

Name ________________________

EXERCISE 19-9

Equivalent units of production:

	CEREAL (IN POUNDS)	BOXES (IN BOXES)	CONVERSION COST (IN BOXES)

Supporting explanation:

EXERCISE 19-10

a.

b.

c.

EXERCISE 19-11

a.

b.

UNITS	WHOLE UNITS	EQUIVALENT UNITS	
		DIRECT MATERIALS	CONVERSION

c.

COSTS	COSTS	
	DIRECT MATERIALS	CONVERSION

d. ______________________________

EXERCISE 19-12

a.

b.

c.

Name ______________________________

EXERCISE 19-13

EXERCISE 19-14

a. ______________________________

b.

UNITS	WHOLE UNITS	EQUIVALENT UNITS	
		DIRECT MATERIALS	CONVERSION

COSTS	COSTS	
	DIRECT MATERIALS	CONVERSION

c. ______________________________

EXERCISE 19-15

a. – e.

EXERCISE 19-16

a.–d.

UNITS	WHOLE UNITS	EQUIVALENT UNITS	
		DIRECT MATERIALS	CONVERSION

EXERCISE 19-16, Concluded

COSTS	COSTS		
	DIRECT MATERIALS	CONVERSION	TOTAL COSTS

EXERCISE 19-17

UNITS	WHOLE UNITS	EQUIVALENT UNITS	
		DIRECT MATERIALS	CONVERSION

EXERCISE 19-17, Concluded

COSTS	COSTS		
	DIRECT MATERIALS	CONVERSION	TOTAL COSTS

EXERCISE 19-18

a. 1.–3.

JOURNAL PAGE

	DATE		DESCRIPTION	POST. REF.	DEBIT	CREDIT	
1							1
2							2
3							3
4							4
5							5
6							6
7							7
8							8
9							9
10							10

Supporting calculations:

b.

EXERCISE 19-19

EXERCISE 19-20

EXERCISE 19-21

APPENDIX EXERCISE 19-22

a. and b.

UNITS	WHOLE UNITS	EQUIVALENT UNITS OF PRODUCTION

APPENDIX EXERCISE 19-23

a. Drawing Department

UNITS	WHOLE UNITS	EQUIVALENT UNITS OF PRODUCTION

APPENDIX EXERCISE 19-23, Concluded

b. Winding Department

UNITS	WHOLE UNITS	EQUIVALENT UNITS OF PRODUCTION

APPENDIX EXERCISE 19-24

a.

b.

UNITS	WHOLE UNITS	EQUIVALENT UNITS OF PRODUCTION

APPENDIX EXERCISE 19-25

a. and b.

UNITS	WHOLE UNITS	EQUIVALENT UNITS OF PRODUCTION

c.

d.

e.

APPENDIX EXERCISE 19-26

a.

UNITS	WHOLE UNITS	EQUIVALENT UNITS OF PRODUCTION

b.

c.

APPENDIX EXERCISE 19-27

UNITS	WHOLE UNITS	EQUIVALENT UNITS OF PRODUCTION

COSTS	COSTS

APPENDIX EXERCISE 19-28

UNITS	WHOLE UNITS	EQUIVALENT UNITS OF PRODUCTION

COSTS	COSTS

PROBLEM 19-1 ___

1. a.–i.

JOURNAL

PAGE

DATE		DESCRIPTION	POST. REF.	DEBIT	CREDIT

PROBLEM 19-1 ___, Concluded

JOURNAL PAGE

	DATE		DESCRIPTION	POST. REF.	DEBIT	CREDIT	
1							1
2							2
3							3
4							4
5							5
6							6

2.

3.

Name ______________________________

PROBLEM 19-2 ___

a.–j.

JOURNAL

PAGE

DATE		DESCRIPTION	POST. REF.	DEBIT	CREDIT

PROBLEM 19-2 ___, Concluded

JOURNAL

PAGE

DATE		DESCRIPTION	POST. REF.	DEBIT	CREDIT

Name ______________________________

PROBLEM 19-3 ___

UNITS	WHOLE UNITS	EQUIVALENT UNITS	
		DIRECT MATERIALS	CONVERSION

PROBLEM 19-3 ___, Continued

COSTS	COSTS		
	DIRECT MATERIALS	CONVERSION	TOTAL COSTS

PROBLEM 19-3___, Concluded

2.

Page not used.

Name ______________________

PROBLEM 19-4 ___

1.

UNITS	WHOLE UNITS	EQUIVALENT UNITS	
		DIRECT MATERIALS	CONVERSION

PROBLEM 19-4 ___, Continued

COSTS	COSTS		
	DIRECT MATERIALS	CONVERSION	TOTAL COSTS

Name ____

PROBLEM 19-4 ___, Continued

2.

JOURNAL

PAGE

DATE		DESCRIPTION	POST. REF.	DEBIT	CREDIT

PROBLEM 19-4 ___, Concluded

3. and 4.

Name ____________________

PROBLEM 19-5 ___

1. and 2.

ACCOUNT *Work in Process—____________ Department* ACCOUNT NO.

DATE		ITEM	POST. REF.	DEBIT	CREDIT	BALANCE	
						DEBIT	CREDIT

PROBLEM 19-5 ___, Continued

1. a. through d.

UNITS	WHOLE UNITS	EQUIVALENT UNITS	
		DIRECT MATERIALS	CONVERSION

PROBLEM 19-5 ___, Continued

COSTS	COSTS		
	DIRECT MATERIALS	CONVERSION	TOTAL COSTS

PROBLEM 19-5 ___, Continued

2.

UNITS	WHOLE UNITS	EQUIVALENT UNITS	
		DIRECT MATERIALS	CONVERSION

Name ______________________________

PROBLEM 19-5 ___, Continued

COSTS	COSTS		
	DIRECT MATERIALS	CONVERSION	TOTAL COSTS

PROBLEM 19-5 ___, Concluded

3.

APPENDIX PROBLEM 19-6___

UNITS	WHOLE UNITS	EQUIVALENT UNITS OF PRODUCTION

APPENDIX PROBLEM 19-6___, Concluded

COSTS	COSTS

APPENDIX PROBLEM 19-7___

UNITS	WHOLE UNITS	EQUIVALENT UNITS OF PRODUCTION

APPENDIX PROBLEM 19-7___, Concluded

COSTS	COSTS

Name ______________________________

EXERCISE 20-1

1. ______________________________
2. ______________________________
3. ______________________________
4. ______________________________
5. ______________________________
6. ______________________________
7. ______________________________
8. ______________________________
9. ______________________________
10. ______________________________
11. ______________________________
12. ______________________________
13. ______________________________
14. ______________________________
15. ______________________________

EXERCISE 20-2

a. ______________________________
b. ______________________________
c. ______________________________
d. ______________________________
e. ______________________________

EXERCISE 20-3

1. Admissions office salaries: ______________________________
2. Record office salaries: ______________________________
3. Housing personnel wages: ______________________________
4. Supplies: ______________________________
5. Instructor salaries: ______________________________
6. Financial aid office salaries: ______________________________

EXERCISE 20-4

1. Preparation costs: ______________________________
2. Salespersons' commission: ______________________________
3. Administrative costs: ______________________________

EXERCISE 20-5

a. ______________________________
b. ______________________________
c. ______________________________
d. ______________________________
e. ______________________________
f. ______________________________
g. ______________________________
h. ______________________________
i. ______________________________
j. ______________________________
k. ______________________________
l. ______________________________

EXERCISE 20-6

	200,000	300,000	400,000
CDs produced	200,000	300,000	400,000
Total costs:			
Total variable costs	$800,000	(d) ________	(j) ________
Total fixed costs	180,000	(e) ________	(k) ________
Total costs	$980,000	(f) ________	(l) ________
Cost per unit:			
Variable cost per unit	(a) ________	(g) ________	(m) ________
Fixed cost per unit	(b) ________	(h) ________	(n) ________
Total cost per unit	(c) ________	(i) ________	(o) ________

Supporting calculations:

EXERCISE 20-7

a. Variable cost per unit: ______________________________

Fixed cost: ______________________________

b. ______________________________

EXERCISE 20-8

Variable cost per gross-ton mile:

Fixed cost:

EXERCISE 20-9

a.

EXERCISE 20-9, Concluded

b. ______________________________

EXERCISE 20-10

a. ______________________________

b. ______________________________

c. ______________________________

EXERCISE 20-11

a.

b.

EXERCISE 20-12

a.

b.

Name ________________________

EXERCISE 20-13

a. ________________________

b. ________________________

EXERCISE 20-14

EXERCISE 20-15

Name ________________________________

EXERCISE 20-16

a.

b.

EXERCISE 20-17

a.

b.

c.

EXERCISE 20-18

a. ______________________________

____

b. ______________________________

____

____

____

____

c.

d. ______________________________

____

____

____

____

EXERCISE 20-19

Chart name: ______________________________

a. ______________________________

b. ______________________________

c. ______________________________

d. ______________________________

e. ______________________________

f. ______________________________

EXERCISE 20-20

Chart name: ______________________________

a. ______________________________

b. ______________________________

c. ______________________________

d. ______________________________

e. ______________________________

f. ______________________________

EXERCISE 20-21

a. ______________________________

b. Potato chips: ______________________________

Pretzels: ______________________________

EXERCISE 20-22

a.

b.

EXERCISE 20-23

a. (1) In dollars:

(2) As a percentage of sales:

b.

EXERCISE 20-24

EXERCISE 20-25

a. Abdel Inc. operating leverage:

Hui Inc. operating leverage:

b.

c.

APPENDIX EXERCISE 20-26

a.

b.

c.

APPENDIX EXERCISE 20-27

Computations:

APPENDIX EXERCISE 20-28

Computations:

Page not used.

Name ____________________

PROBLEM 20-1 ___

Cost	Fixed Cost	Variable Cost	Mixed Cost
a.			
b.			
c.			
d.			
e.			
f.			
g.			
h.			
i.			
j.			
k.			
l.			
m.			
n.			
o.			
p.			
q.			
r.			
s.			
t.			

Page not used.

Name ______________________________

PROBLEM 20-2 ___

1. *Omit "00" in the cents columns.*

	FIXED COSTS	VARIABLE COSTS

2. a. Unit variable cost: ______________________________

b. Unit contribution margin: ______________________________

3. ______________________________

4. ______________________________

5. ______________________________

PROBLEM 20-2 ___, Concluded

6. ___

7. ___

8. ___

Name ______________________________

PROBLEM 20-3 ___

1. Break-even sales (units):

2. Sales (units):

PROBLEM 20-3 ___, Concluded

3.

Sales and Costs

Units of Sales

4. ____

____

____

____

Name ____

PROBLEM 20-4 ___

1.

Sales and Costs

Units of Sales

2. a. ____

____

____

____

b. ____

____

____

____

PROBLEM 20-4 ___, Concluded

3.

Sales and Costs

Units of Sales

4. a. ______________________________

____

____

____

b. ______________________________

____

____

____

Name ______________________________

PROBLEM 20-5 ___

1. ______________________________

2. ______________________________

3. ______________________________

Page not used.

PROBLEM 20-6 ___

1. *Omit "00" in the cents columns.*

Estimated Income Statement

For the Year Ending December 31, 2006

PROBLEM 20-6 ___, Continued

2.

3.

Name ____

PROBLEM 20-6 ___, Continued

4.

Sales and Costs

Units of Sales

PROBLEM 20-6 ___, Concluded

5. ______________________________

6. ______________________________

EXERCISE 21-1

a.

Hakim Davis

Cash Budget

For the Four Months Ending December 31, 2006

	SEPTEMBER	OCTOBER	NOVEMBER	DECEMBER

b.

c.

EXERCISE 21-2

Central Industrial Supply

Flexible Selling and Administrative Expenses Budget

For the Month Ending May 31, 2006

EXERCISE 21-3

a.

Towers Company—Molding Department

Flexible Production Budget

For the Three Months Ending March 31, 2006

	JANUARY	FEBRUARY	MARCH

b.

	JANUARY	FEBRUARY	MARCH

Comparison suggests . . .

EXERCISE 21-4

Steelcase Corporation
Fabrication Department
May 2006
(assumed data)

EXERCISE 21-5

a.

Harmony Audio Company
Sales Budget
For the Month Ending September 30, 2007

PRODUCT AND AREA	UNIT SALES VOLUME	UNIT SELLING PRICE	TOTAL SALES

EXERCISE 21-5, Concluded

b.

Harmony Audio Company
Production Budget
For the Month Ending September 30, 2007

	UNITS	
	MODEL DL	MODEL XL

EXERCISE 21-6

Jeffries and Valdez, CPAs
Professional Fees Budget
For the Year Ending December 31, 2006

	BILLABLE HOURS	HOURLY RATE	TOTAL REVENUE

EXERCISE 21-7

Jeffries and Valdez, CPAs

Professional Labor Cost Budget

For the Year Ending December 31, 2006

	BILLABLE HOURS REQUIRED	
	STAFF	PARTNERS

EXERCISE 21-8

Taste of Italy Frozen Pizza Inc.

Direct Materials Purchases Budget

For the Month Ending August 31, 2006

	DOUGH	TOMATO	CHEESE	TOTAL

EXERCISE 21-9

Coca-Cola Enterprises—Chattanooga Plant
Direct Materials Purchases Budget
For the Month Ending September 30, 2006
(assumed data)

	CONCENTRATE	2-LITER BOTTLES	CARBONATED WATER

EXERCISE 21-10

Goodman Tire Company
Direct Materials Purchases Budget
For the Year Ending December 31, 2006

	RUBBER	STEEL BELTS	TOTAL

EXERCISE 21-11

Ace Racket Company

Direct Labor Cost Budget

For the Month Ending August 31, 2006

	FORMING DEPARTMENT	ASSEMBLY DEPARTMENT

EXERCISE 21-12

City Suites Hotels, Inc.

Direct Labor Cost Budget

For a Weekday and a Weekend Day

	WEEKDAY	WEEKEND DAY

EXERCISE 21-13

a.

Levi Strauss & Co.

Production Budget

March 2006

(assumed data)

	DOCKERS®	501 JEANS®

b.

Levi Strauss & Co.

Direct Labor Cost Budget

March 2006

(assumed data)

	INSEAM	OUTERSEAM	POCKETS	ZIPPER

EXERCISE 21-14

Dutch Shoe Company

Factory Overhead Cost Budget

For the Month Ending January 31, 2006

EXERCISE 21-15

Union Chemical Company

Cost of Goods Sold Budget

For the Month Ending April 30, 20--

EXERCISE 21-16

Heritage Ceramic Company

Cost of Goods Sold Budget

For the Month Ending June 30, 2006

EXERCISE 21-17

Lion Heart Company

Schedule of Collections from Sales

For the Three Months Ending May 31, 2006

	MARCH	APRIL	MAY

EXERCISE 21-18

Star Office Supplies Inc.

Schedule of Collections from Sales

For the Three Months Ending March 31, 2006

	JANUARY	FEBRUARY	MARCH

EXERCISE 21-19

Distance Learning Systems Inc.

Schedule of Cash Payments for Selling and Administrative Expenses

For the Three Months Ending August 31, 2006

	JUNE	JULY	AUGUST

EXERCISE 21-20

Zone Fitness Center

Schedule of Cash Payments for Operations

For the Three Months Ending December 31, 2007

	OCTOBER	NOVEMBER	DECEMBER

EXERCISE 21-21

O'Brien Manufacturing Company

Capital Expenditures Budget

For the Four Years Ending December 31, 2005–2008

	2005	2006	2007	2008

PROBLEM 21-1 ___

1.

	UNIT SALES, YEAR ENDED 2006		INCREASE (DECREASE) ACTUAL OVER BUDGET	
	BUDGET	ACTUAL SALES	AMOUNT	PERCENT

2.

	2006 ACTUAL UNITS	PERCENTAGE INCREASE (DECREASE)	2007 BUDGETED UNITS

PROBLEM 21-1 ___, Concluded

3.

Sales Budget

For the Year Ending December 31, 2007

PRODUCT AND AREA	UNITS SALES VOLUME	UNIT SELLING PRICE	TOTAL SALES

Name ______________________________

PROBLEM 21-2 ___

1.

Sales Budget

PRODUCT AND AREA	UNITS SALES VOLUME	UNIT SELLING PRICE	TOTAL SALES

2.

Production Budget

	UNITS	

PROBLEM 21-3 ___

1.

Sales Budget

	UNITS SALES VOLUME	UNIT SELLING PRICE	TOTAL SALES

2.

Production Budget

	UNITS	

PROBLEM 21-3 ___, Continued

3.

Direct Materials Purchases Budget

	DIRECT MATERIALS		TOTAL

4.

Direct Labor Cost Budget

	DEPARTMENT	DEPARTMENT	TOTAL

PROBLEM 21-3 ___, Continued

5.

Factory Overhead Cost Budget

PROBLEM 21-3 ___, Continued

6.

Cost of Goods Sold Budget

PROBLEM 21-3 ___, Continued

7.

Selling and Administrative Expenses Budget

PROBLEM 21-3 ___, Concluded

8.

Budgeted Income Statement

PROBLEM 21-4 ___

1. *Omit "00" in the cents columns.*

Cash Budget

PROBLEM 21-4 ___, Concluded

Computations:

2.

PROBLEM 21-5 ___

1. *Omit "00" in the cents columns.*

Budgeted Income Statement

For the Year Ending December 31, 2007

PROBLEM 21-5 ___, Concluded

2. *Omit "00" in the cents columns.*

Budgeted Balance Sheet

December 31, 2007

Name ____

EXERCISE 22-1

EXERCISE 22-2

EXERCISE 22-3

a.

Sams Bottle Company

Manufacturing Cost Budget

For the Month Ended July 31, 2006

	STANDARD COST AT PLANNED VOLUME (600,000 BOTTLES)

b.

Sams Bottle Company

Manufacturing Costs—Budget Performance Report

For the Month Ended July 31, 2006

	ACTUAL COSTS	STANDARD COST AT ACTUAL VOLUME (640,000 BOTTLES)	COST VARIANCE—(FAVORABLE) UNFAVORABLE

c.

Name ________________________________

EXERCISE 22-4

a.

b.

EXERCISE 22-5

EXERCISE 22-6

a.

b.

EXERCISE 22-7

a.

b.

EXERCISE 22-8

a. Direct labor rate variance:

Direct labor time variance:

b. Direct labor debited to Work in Process:

EXERCISE 22-9

EXERCISE 22-10

Jarrett Wood Products Company

Factory Overhead Cost Budget—Press Department

For the Month Ended March 31, 2006

EXERCISE 22-11

EXERCISE 22-12

a. Variable factory overhead controllable variance:

b. Fixed factory overhead volume variance:

EXERCISE 22-13

Tri-State Molded Products Inc.

Factory Overhead Cost Variance Report—Trim Department

For the Month Ended July 31, 2006

Productive capacity for the month:

Actual productive capacity used for the month:

	BUDGET (AT ACTUAL PRODUCTION)	ACTUAL	VARIANCES	
			FAVORABLE	UNFAVORABLE

EXERCISE 22-14

a. and b.

JOURNAL PAGE

	DATE		DESCRIPTION	POST. REF.	DEBIT	CREDIT	
1							1
2							2
3							3
4							4
5							5
6							6
7							7
8							8

EXERCISE 22-15

Beartooth Company

Income Statement

For the Month Ended January 31, 2006

	FAVORABLE	UNFAVORABLE	

EXERCISE 22-16

EXERCISE 22-17

a.

b.

c.

EXERCISE 22-18

a.

b.

EXERCISE 22-19

a. Input Measures:

EXERCISE 22-19, Concluded

Output Measures:

b.

EXERCISE 22-20

	Input Measure	Output Measure
Average computer response time to customer "clicks"		
Dollar amount of returned goods		
Elapsed time between customer order and product delivery		
Maintenance dollars divided by hardware investment		
Number of customer complaints divided by the number of orders		
Number of misfilled orders		
Number of orders per warehouse employee		
Number of page faults or errors due to software programming errors		
Server (computer) downtime		
System capacity divided by customer demands		
Training dollars per programmer		

PROBLEM 22-1 ___

a.–c.

PROBLEM 22-1 ___, Concluded

PROBLEM 22-2 ___

1. a. *Omit "00" in the cents columns.*

			TOTAL

PROBLEM 22-2 ___, Concluded

1. b. *Omit "00" in the cents columns.*

			TOTAL

2.

PROBLEM 22-3 ___

a.

b.

PROBLEM 22-3 ___, Concluded

c.

Name ______________________________

PROBLEM 22-4 ___

Factory Overhead Cost Variance Report—____________________ Department

Normal capacity for the month:

Actual production for the month:

	BUDGET	ACTUAL	VARIANCES	
			FAVORABLE	UNFAVORABLE

Page not used.

Name ______________________________________

PROBLEM 22-5 ___

1.–6.

PROBLEM 22-5 ___, Concluded

EXERCISE 23-1

a.

Air-Cool Company
Budget Performance Report—Vice-President, Production
For the Month Ended April 30, 2006

Plant	Budget	Actual	Over Budget	Under Budget
St. Louis Plant	$258,900	$257,800		$1,100
Tempe Plant	185,700	184,700		1,000
Syracuse Plant	(g) ______	(h) ______	(i) $ ______	______
	(j) $ ______	(k) $ ______	(l) $ ______	$2,100

Air-Cool Company
Budget Performance Report—Manager, Syracuse Plant
For the Month Ended April 30, 2006

Department	Budget	Actual	Over Budget	Under Budget
Compressor Assembly	(a) $ ______	(b) $ ______	(c) $ ______	
Electronic Assembly	53,200	53,900	700	
Final Assembly	85,700	85,400	______	$300
	(d) $ ______	(e) $ ______	(f) $ ______	$300

b.

EXERCISE 23-2

Hi-Volt Electrical Equipment Company

Divisional Income Statements

For the Year Ended June 30, 2006

	RESIDENTIAL DIVISION	INDUSTRIAL DIVISION

EXERCISE 23-3

a. Duplication services: ____________________

b. Accounts receivable: ____________________

c. Electronic data processing: ____________________

d. Central purchasing: ____________________

e. Legal: ____________________

f. Telecommunications: ____________________

EXERCISE 23-4

a. Accounts Receivable: ______________________________

b. Conferences: ______________________________

c. Payroll Accounting: ______________________________

d. Telecommunications: ______________________________

e. Employee Travel: ______________________________

f. Computer Support: ______________________________

g. Training: ______________________________

h. Central Purchasing: ______________________________

EXERCISE 23-5

a.

EXERCISE 23-5, Concluded

b.

EXERCISE 23-6

a. Help desk:

Network center:

Electronic mail:

Local voice support:

b. Help desk:

Network center:

Electronic mail:

Local voice support:

Name ______________________________

EXERCISE 23-7

Entertainment Electronics Company

Divisional Income Statements

For the Year Ended December 31, 2006

	VIDEO DIVISION		AUDIO DIVISION	

EXERCISE 23-8

a.

b.

Pegasus Airlines Inc.
Divisional Income Statements
For the Year Ended October 31, 2006

	PASSENGER DIVISION	CARGO DIVISION

EXERCISE 23-9

Sierra Sporting Goods Co.
Divisional Income Statements
For the Year Ended June 30, 2006

	CAMPING EQUIPMENT DIVISION	SKI EQUIPMENT DIVISION

Supporting Schedule:

Service Department Charges

	CAMPING DIVISION	SKI DIVISION	TOTAL

EXERCISE 23-10

a. Cheese Division: ____________________

Milk Division: ____________________

Butter Division: ____________________

b. ____________________

EXERCISE 23-11

a.

	CHEESE DIVISION	MILK DIVISION	BUTTER DIVISION

b.

EXERCISE 23-12

Rate of return on investment	=	Profit margin	×	Investment turnover
21%	=	15%	×	(a) ________
(b) ________	=	8%	×	1.75
18%	=	(c) ________	×	0.75
27%	=	18%	×	(d) ________
(e) ________	=	12%	×	2.0

EXERCISE 23-13

a. ______________________

b. ______________________

EXERCISE 23-14

a.

b.

Name ______________________________

EXERCISE 23-15

(a)

(b) ______________________________

(c) ______________________________

(d) ______________________________

(e) ______________________________

(f) ______________________________

(g) ______________________________

(h) ______________________________

(i) ______________________________

(j) ______________________________

(k) ______________________________

(l) ______________________________

EXERCISE 23-16

a. **(a)** ______________________________

(b) ______________________________

(c) ______________________________

(d) ______________________________

(e) ______________________________

(f) ______________________________

(g) ______________________________

(h) ______________________________

(i) ______________________________

(j) ______________________________

(k) ______________________________

(l) ______________________________

b. North Division: ______________________________

East Division: ______________________________

South Division: ______________________________

West Division: ______________________________

c. **(1)** ______________________________

____

____

(2) ______________________________

____

____

____

EXERCISE 23-17

a.

b.

c.

EXERCISE 23-18

Average cardmember spending: ______________________

____

____

Cards in force: ______________________

____

____

Earnings growth: ______________________

____

____

Hours of credit consultant training: ______________________

____

____

Investment in information technology: ______________________

____

____

Number of Internet features: ______________________

____

____

Number of merchant signings: ______________________

____

____

Number of card choices: ______________________

____

____

Number of new card launches: ______________________

____

____

Return on equity: ______________________

____

____

Revenue growth: ______________________

____

____

EXERCISE 23-19

a.

b.

EXERCISE 23-20

a. ______________________________

b. ______________________________

c. ______________________________

EXERCISE 23-21

a.

b.

c.

d.

PROBLEM 23-1 ___

1.

	BUDGET	ACTUAL	OVER BUDGET	UNDER BUDGET

PROBLEM 23-1 ___, Concluded

2.

PROBLEM 23-2 ___

1.

Divisional Income Statements

Supporting schedules:

PROBLEM 23-2 ___, Concluded

2.

3.

PROBLEM 23-3 ___

1.

Divisional Income Statements

PROBLEM 23-3 ___, Concluded

2.

3.

PROBLEM 23-4 ___

1.

2.

Estimated Income Statements

	PROPOSAL 1	PROPOSAL 2	PROPOSAL 3

PROBLEM 23-4 ___, Concluded

3.

4.

5.

PROBLEM 23-5 ___

1.

Divisional Income Statements

2.

PROBLEM 23-5 ___, Concluded

3.

4.

PROBLEM 23-6 ___

1.

2.

PROBLEM 23-6 ___, Continued

3.

Divisional Income Statements

			TOTAL

Name ______________________________________

PROBLEM 23-6 ___, Continued

4.

PROBLEM 23-6 ___, Concluded

5. a. and b.

EXERCISE 24-1

a.

Tenney Construction Company
Proposal to Lease or Sell Machinery
January 3, 2006

b. ______________________________

EXERCISE 24-2

a.

Nordic Beverage Inc.
Proposal to Discontinue Diet Kola
January 3, 2006

b. ______________________________

EXERCISE 24-3

a.

Century Ceramics Company
Differential Product Analysis Report
For the Year Ended December 31, 2006

	BOWLS	PLATES	CUPS

b.

EXERCISE 24-4

a.

Name ______________________________

EXERCISE 24-4, Concluded

b.

c.

	INDIVIDUAL INVESTOR	INSTITUTIONAL INVESTOR	CAPITAL MARKETS

d.

EXERCISE 24-5

EXERCISE 24-6

a.

Advent Computer Company

Proposal to Manufacture Carrying Case

June 5, 2006

b.

EXERCISE 24-7

a.

International Pet Association

Proposal to Purchase Outside Layout Services

December 15, 2005

b.

c.

EXERCISE 24-8

a.

b.

EXERCISE 24-9

a.

IC Electronics Company

Proposal to Replace Machine

January 20, 2006

EXERCISE 24-9, Concluded

b. ______________________________

c. ______________________________

EXERCISE 24-10

a. Differential revenue: ______________________________

b. Differential cost: ______________________________

c. Differential income: ______________________________

EXERCISE 24-11

a.

AM Coffee Company

Proposal to Process Columbian Coffee Further

EXERCISE 24-11, Concluded

b.

c.

EXERCISE 24-12

a.

Outdoor Denim Co.

Proposal to Sell to Barker Company

January 18, 2006

EXERCISE 24-12, Concluded

b.

c.

EXERCISE 24-13

EXERCISE 24-14

a.

Dunkirk Tire and Rubber Company

Proposal to Sell to Continental Motors

August 4, 2006

b.

EXERCISE 24-15

a.

b.

c.

d.

EXERCISE 24-16

a.

b.

EXERCISE 24-16, Continued

c. ______________________

EXERCISE 24-17

a. ______________________

b. ______________________

c. ______________________

EXERCISE 24-18

a. ______________________

b. ______________________

EXERCISE 24-19

a.

b.

c.

EXERCISE 24-20

EXERCISE 24-21

a.

	LARGE	MEDIUM	SMALL	TOTAL

b. ________________________________

EXERCISE 24-22

EXERCISE 24-22, Concluded

APPENDIX EXERCISE 24-23

APPENDIX EXERCISE 24-24

a.

b.

APPENDIX EXERCISE 24-24, Concluded

c.

d.

PROBLEM 24-1 ___

1. *Omit "00" in the cents columns.*

Proposal to Operate ____________________

PROBLEM 24-1 ___, Concluded

2.

3.

PROBLEM 24-2 ___

1. *Omit "00" in the cents columns.*

Proposal to Replace Machine

PROBLEM 24-2 ___, Concluded

2.

PROBLEM 24-3 ___

1. *Omit "00" in the cents columns.*

Proposals for Sales Promotion Campaign

PROBLEM 24-3 ___, Concluded

2.

Name ______________________________________

PROBLEM 24-4 ___

1. *Omit "00" in the cents columns.*

Proposal to Process ____________________ Further

PROBLEM 24-4 ___, Concluded

2.

PROBLEM 24-5 ___

1. ____

2. a. ____

____

____

____

____

b. ____

____

____

____

____

____

____

c. ____

____

____

3. a. ____

____

____

____

____

b. ____

____

____

____

____

____

____

____

____

____

____

____

c. ____

____

____

PROBLEM 24-5 ___, Concluded

4. a. ______________________________

b. ______________________________

c. ______________________________

5. ______________________________

6. a. *Omit "00" in the cents columns.*

Proposal to Sell to ____________________

b. ______________________________

PROBLEM 24-6 ___

1. *Omit "00" in the cents columns.*

2. *Omit "00" in the cents columns.*

Explanation:

PROBLEM 24-6 ___, Concluded

3.

EXERCISE 25-1

EXERCISE 25-2

EXERCISE 25-3

EXERCISE 25-4

	YEAR 1	YEARS 2–14	LAST YEAR

Name ______________________________

EXERCISE 25-5

EXERCISE 25-6

a.

b.

EXERCISE 25-7

a.

Year	Present Value of $1 at 12%	Net Cash Flow	Present Value of Net Cash Flow
1			
2			
3			
4			
Total			
Amount to be invested			
Net present value			

b. ______________________________

____

EXERCISE 25-8

a. 2006 cash flow:

____

____

____

____

2007 home video sales:

____

____

____

____

____

Year	Present Value of $1 at 15%	Net Cash Flow	Present Value of Net Cash Flow
1			
2			
3			
4			
Total			
Amount to be invested			
Net present value			

EXERCISE 25-8, Concluded

b.

EXERCISE 25-9

a.

b.

c.

EXERCISE 25-10

Apartment Complex:

Year	Present Value of $1 at 15%	Net Cash Flow	Present Value of Net Cash Flow
1			
2			
3			
4			
Residual value			
Total			
Amount to be invested			
Net present value			

Office Building:

Year	Present Value of $1 at 15%	Net Cash Flow	Present Value of Net Cash Flow
1			
2			
3			
4			
Total			
Amount to be invested			
Net present value			

Conclusion with explanation:

EXERCISE 25-11

EXERCISE 25-12

a. ______________________________

b. ______________________________

c. ______________________________

EXERCISE 25-13

EXERCISE 25-14

a.

EXERCISE 25-14, Concluded

b.

c.

EXERCISE 25-15

a.

b.

EXERCISE 25-15, Concluded

c. ______________________

EXERCISE 25-16

a. ______________________

b. ______________________

EXERCISE 25-17

EXERCISE 25-18

a. Delivery Truck:

Bagging Machine:

b.

EXERCISE 25-19

a.

b.

c.

EXERCISE 25-20

EXERCISE 25-21

a.

b.

PROBLEM 25-1 ___

1. a. ______________________________

____

____

____

____

b.

Year	Present Value of $1 at _____%	Net Cash Flow		Present Value of Net Cash Flow	
		Project ________	Project ________	Project ________	Project ________
1					
2					
3					
4					
5					
Total...............................					
Amount to be invested..					
Net present value					

2.

____

PROBLEM 25-1 ___, Concluded

PROBLEM 25-2 ___

1. a. ________________________________

____

____

____

____

b.

Year	Present Value of $1 at _____%	Net Cash Flow		Present Value of Net Cash Flow	
		Project ______	Project ______	Project ______	Project ______
1					
2					
3					
4					
5					
Total...............................					
Amount to be invested..					
Net present value					

2.

____

____

____

____

____

____

____

____

____

____

____

____

____

____

____

____

____

PROBLEM 25-2 ___, Concluded

PROBLEM 25-3 ___

1. Proposal (Project) ____:

Year	Present Value of $1 at _____%	Net Cash Flow	Present Value of Net Cash Flow
1			
2			
3			
Total			
Amount to be invested			
Net present value			

Proposal (Project) ____:

Year	Present Value of $1 at _____%	Net Cash Flow	Present Value of Net Cash Flow
1			
2			
3			
Total			
Amount to be invested			
Net present value			

Proposal (Project) ____:

Year	Present Value of $1 at _____%	Net Cash Flow	Present Value of Net Cash Flow
1			
2			
3			
Total			
Amount to be invested			
Net present value			

PROBLEM 25-3 ___, Concluded

2.

3.

PROBLEM 25-4 ___

1. a. and b.

PROBLEM 25-4 ___, Concluded

2. a. and b.

3.

Name ____________________

PROBLEM 25-5 ___

1.

2.

Year	Present Value of $1 at 15%	Net Cash Flow		Present Value of Net Cash Flow	
		Project ______	Project ______	Project ______	Project ______
1					
2					
3					
4					
Residual value					
Total					
Amount to be invested					
Net present value					

PROBLEM 25-5 ___, Concluded

3.

PROBLEM 25-6 ___

1.

Proposal A:

Proposal B:

Proposal C:

PROBLEM 25-6 ___, Continued

Proposal D:

2.

Proposal A:

Proposal B:

Proposal C:

Proposal D:

Name ______________________________________

PROBLEM 25-6 ___, Continued

3.

Proposal	Cash Payback Period	Average Rate of Return	Accept for Further Analysis	Reject
A				
B				
C				
D				

4. Proposal ___:

Year	Present Value of $1 at 10%	Net Cash Flow	Present Value of Net Cash Flow
1			
2			
3			
4			
5			
Total..........			
Amount to be invested..........			
Net present value			

Proposal ___:

Year	Present Value of $1 at 10%	Net Cash Flow	Present Value of Net Cash Flow
1			
2			
3			
4			
5			
Total..........			
Amount to be invested..........			
Net present value			

PROBLEM 25-6 ___, Concluded

5.

6.

7.

8.

Name ______________________________

EXERCISE D-1

JOURNAL PAGE

DATE		DESCRIPTION	POST. REF.	DEBIT	CREDIT

EXERCISE D-2

JOURNAL

PAGE

DATE	DESCRIPTION	POST. REF.	DEBIT	CREDIT

Name ______________________________________

PROBLEM D-1

1. and 2.

JOURNAL

PAGE

	DATE	DESCRIPTION	POST. REF.	DEBIT	CREDIT	

PROBLEM D-1, Concluded

JOURNAL

PAGE

DATE	DESCRIPTION	POST. REF.	DEBIT	CREDIT

JOURNAL

PAGE

DATE		DESCRIPTION	POST. REF.	DEBIT	CREDIT

JOURNAL

PAGE

	DATE	DESCRIPTION	POST. REF.	DEBIT	CREDIT	
1						1
2						2
3						3
4						4
5						5
6						6
7						7
8						8
9						9
10						10
11						11
12						12
13						13
14						14
15						15
16						16
17						17
18						18
19						19
20						20
21						21
22						22
23						23
24						24
25						25
26						26
27						27
28						28
29						29
30						30
31						31
32						32
33						33
34						34
35						35
36						36
37						37

Name ______________________________

Name ____________________